W9-BMP-817

Literature

and the Language Arts

The American Tradition

SPEAKING AND LISTENING

THE EMC MASTERPIECE SERIES

EMCParadigm Publishing Saint Paul, Minnesota

Staff Credits

Editorial

Laurie Skiba
Editor

Brenda Owens
Associate Editor

Lori Ann Coleman
Associate Editor

Diana Moen
Associate Editor

Gia Marie Garbinsky
Assistant Editor

Jennifer Joline Anderson
Assistant Editor

Janice Johnson
Curriculum Specialist

Paul Spencer
Art and Photo Researcher

Chris Bohen
Editorial Assistant

Chris Nelson
Editorial Assistant

Katherine S. Link
Editorial Assistant

Design

Shelley Clubb
Production Manager

C. Vern Johnson
Senior Designer

Cover Credits

Cover Designer: C. Vern Johnson

Watson and the Shark [Detail], 1778. John Singleton Copley. Museum of Fine Arts, Boston.

Aspects of Negro Life: From Slavery through Reconstruction [Detail], 1934. Aaron Douglas. Schomberg Center for Research in Black Culture, New York.

Something on the Eight Ball [Detail], 1953. Stuart Davis. Philadelphia Museum of Art.

ISBN 0-8219-2172-X
© 2001 EMC Corporation

All rights reserved. No part of this publication may be adapted, reproduced, stored in a retrieval system, or transmitted in any form or by any means, electronic, mechanical, photocopying, recording, or otherwise without permission from the publisher.

Published by EMC/Paradigm Publishing
875 Montreal Way
St. Paul, Minnesota 55102
800-328-1452
www.emcp.com
E-mail: educate@emcp.com

Printed in the United States of America.
10 9 8 7 6 5 4 3 2 XXX 02 03 04 05 06 07 08 09

Contents

THE POWER OF COMMUNICATION 1

4.1 Verbal and Nonverbal Communication 1

LISTENING SKILLS 2

4.2 Active versus Passive Listening 2

4.3 Listening to a Lecture or Demonstration 4

4.4 Listening in Conversations 5

4.5 Listening to the Media 6

4.6 Adapting Listening Skills to Specific Tasks 8

COMMUNICATING WITH OTHERS 9

4.7 Communicating with Another Person 9

4.8 Communicating in a Small Group 10

4.9 Communicating in a Large Group 11

4.10 Asking and Answering Questions 13

COMMUNICATION STYLES AND CULTURAL BARRIERS 15

4.11 Being Considerate of Other Cultures and Communication Styles 15

4.12 Overcoming Barriers to Effective Multicultural Communication 16

4.13 Collaborative Learning and Communication 18

4.14 Conducting an Interview 20

PUBLIC SPEAKING 22

4.15 Giving a Speech 22

4.16 Types of Speeches 24

4.17 Steps in Preparing an Extemporaneous Speech 26

4.18 Guidelines for Giving a Speech 28

4.19 Oral Interpretation 30

4.20 Telling a Story 32

4.21 Participating in a Debate 34

4.22 Preparing a Multimedia Presentation 36

ANSWER KEY 39

The Power of Communication

4.1 VERBAL AND NONVERBAL COMMUNICATION

Elements of **verbal communication** include *volume* (loudness or softness), *melody* or *pitch* (highness or lowness), *pace* (speed), *tone* (emotional quality), and *enunciation* (clearness). When speaking to an audience, you can make your speech more effective by

- speaking loudly enough to be heard
- enunciating clearly
- varying your volume, melody or pitch, pace, and tone to suit the different parts of your message

Elements of **nonverbal communication** include *eye contact* (looking audience members in the eye), *facial expression* (using your face to show emotions), *gesture* (meaningful motions of your hands and arms), *posture* (position of the body), and *proximity* (distance from the audience). When standing in front of an audience, you can make your speech more effective by

- making regular eye contact with audience members
- using facial expressions, gestures, posture, and proximity to emphasize your message

EXERCISES

A. Using Elements of Verbal Communication

Work with a partner. Have your partner choose a short poem from your textbook. As your partner reads the poem, rate his or her use of the elements of verbal communication. Use 4 for *excellent,* 3 for *good,* 2 for *average,* and 1 for *needs improvement.* After you have rated your partner's reading, share the results. Ask your partner to read the poem again, paying special attention to the elements you felt could be improved. Finally, select a poem to read. Have your partner rate your verbal communication in the same way.

Volume _____

Melody or Pitch_____

Pace _____

Tone _____

Enunciation _____

B. Communicating Nonverbally

Describe some ways to communicate the following messages nonverbally.

anger: _____

curiosity: _____

fear: _____

nervousness: _____

Listening Skills

4.2 ACTIVE VERSUS PASSIVE LISTENING

Active listening requires skill, concentration, and practice. It doesn't just "happen" on its own. To become an active listener, practice these techniques:

- Don't dominate conversations.
- Show you are listening through eye contact, body language, and facial expressions.
- Think about what the other person has said before responding.
- Don't make assumptions or jump to conclusions about what the other person says.
- Provide feedback as you listen. Rephrase what the speaker has said.
- Control your emotions.

EXERCISES

A. Listening Actively

Read the following dialogue. On the lines below each section, write suggestions about how Mikayla might listen more actively to Andrey.

1. Andrey: Mikayla, you know a lot about computers. Do you know what I should do to get this document to print? I keep selecting the print option but nothing happens.

   Mikayla: Computers can be so frustrating! I remember one time I had to reboot six times before the stupid machine would let me download a song from the Internet.

   _____

   _____

   _____

2. Andrey: Do you think the problem might be that there are too many documents waiting in the print queue? How do I check that?

   Mikayla: (looking in her backpack) Isn't *queue* a weird word? I don't know why the software companies don't just call it a print *line*. What do they think we are anyway? English people lining up to get on a bus? Give me a break!

   _____

   _____

   _____

3. Andrey: Maybe I'll just have to give up printing this document. I guess maybe I could save it on a disk and print it when I get home.

Mikayla: When you get home, could you do me a favor? I want to read an article in last week's issue of *Sports Illustrated,* and I know you keep old copies sometimes.

_____

_____

_____

_____

4. Andrey: Geez, I wish I could get some help on this. I know it's probably just some simple thing, but I—

Mikayla: —Hey, there goes Dina Murray! Hey Dina, congratulations on acing the algebra test. Everybody's talking about it!

_____

_____

_____

B. Rewriting the Dialogue

On the lines below, rewrite the dialogue between Andrey and Mikayla. This time, replace Mikayla's answers with ones that show her listening actively. Use the techniques listed at the top of this page.

_____

_____

_____

_____

_____

_____

_____

_____

_____

_____

_____

_____

_____

_____

4.3 LISTENING TO A LECTURE OR DEMONSTRATION

Listening to a lecture or a demonstration can be challenging. To get the most out of this special situation, try to master these listening skills:

- Think of reasons to listen. Ask yourself "How can I use this information?"
- Let the speaker know you are listening by sitting up straight, making eye contact, and nodding when you agree or understand.
- Listen for the major ideas.
- Take notes on important ideas and supporting details.
- Save questions for later.
- Stay focused on what the speaker is saying. Don't daydream or become distracted.

EXERCISE

Listening to a Lecture

Working in a small group, choose Joan Didion's essay, "On the Mall" (page 916) or Daniel Boorstin's essay, "Why I Am Optimistic about America" (page 1005) from your textbook. Have a person from your group read a page or so of the selection. Listen carefully, as if you were listening to a speaker in an auditorium. After the reader has finished, answer the questions below.

1. How can you use the information included in the reading you just heard?

   _____

   _____

2. At what point in the speech did you nod in agreement or understanding, make eye contact with the speaker, or show in another way that you were listening?

   _____

   _____

3. List the major ideas of the speech, along with a detail that supports each idea.

   Major idea: _____

   Detail: _____

   Major idea: _____

   Detail: _____

   Major idea: _____

   Detail: _____

4. What are three questions you'd like to ask about the selection?

   _____

   _____

   _____

4.4   LISTENING IN CONVERSATIONS

Chances are, the most common situation in which you'll use your listening skills is in conversations—with friends, relatives, teachers, and the many other people you come into contact with every day. Here are some tips to help you be an effective listener in conversations.

- Don't monopolize the conversation; give the other person a chance to talk.
- Use active listening skills when others are talking to show you are paying attention.
- Don't mentally argue; withhold judgment until the other person has finished speaking.
- Ask questions to start a conversation, keep one going, and to show you are really listening.
- Think about what the other person is saying. When you speak respond to the other person's statements.
- Avoid becoming overly emotional.

EXERCISE

Writing a Dialogue

In the space below, write a dialogue between two people to illustrate "Dos" and "Don'ts" in listening in conversations. Then exchange dialogues with a partner and point out the "Dos" and "Don'ts" illustrated in your partner's dialogue.

Person 1: _____

_____

Person 2: _____

_____

Person 1: _____

_____

Person 2: _____

_____

Person 1: _____

_____

Person 2: _____

_____

Person 1: _____

_____

Person 2: _____

_____

Person 1: _____

_____

Person 2: _____

_____

4.5 LISTENING TO THE MEDIA

One area in which it is especially important to be an effective listener is the media. Television, radio, and movies can be powerful influences on viewers and listeners. In order to become an effective listener to the media, use these techniques to think critically and evaluate the messages you hear.

- Learn to distinguish facts from opinions. **Facts** are statements that can be proved by checking a reference work or making observations. **Opinions** express personal beliefs.

- Evaluate an entertainment program's quality as you watch. Consider the acting, directing, and writing, along with production qualities such as lighting, sound effects, staging, camera work, music, and other elements. All of these affect the message the program is sending.

- Think about the ideas and messages the program is sending. Do you agree with them? Why or why not?

- Be choosy about what you watch and listen to. If a program doesn't meet the standards you set, turn it off.

- Limit the amount of time you spend listening to or watching the broadcast media.

EXERCISE

Evaluating a Media Program

The form on the following page will help you evaluate a media program. First choose a program to evaluate, such as a TV news magazine, news broadcast, or entertainment show, or a radio program. Then watch or listen to the show and fill in the blanks.

Name of program _____   Type of program _____

Does the show express facts and/or opinions? Give examples.

_____

_____

_____

_____

How do I rate the program's quality?

Element _____   Evaluation _____

_____   _____

_____   _____

_____   _____

What message(s) does this show send?

Message   Do I agree or not? Why?

_____   _____

_____   _____

_____   _____

_____   _____

Overall evaluation: Would I watch or listen to this show again? Explain.

_____

_____

_____

_____

_____

_____

_____

4.6   ADAPTING LISTENING SKILLS TO SPECIFIC TASKS

Different activities call for different kinds of listening. An effective listener uses different listening strategies in different situations. Four of the most important specific tasks you'll use your listening skills on are

- listening for comprehension (listening to understand information)
- listening critically (listening to comprehend and evaluate a message)
- listening to learn vocabulary (listening to learn new words and how to use them)
- listening for appreciation (listening for enjoyment or entertainment)

EXERCISE

Adapting Listening Skills

In the left-hand column of the table below, you'll find examples of four situations that require four different kinds of listening skills and strategies. Review the information on page 1089 of your textbook. Then complete the table.

SITUATION	KIND OF LISTENING SKILL	OTHER EXAMPLES
1. listening to a political campaign speech		
2. receiving directions on how to play a complex electronic game		
3. discussion of new Internet transmission technologies		
4. discussion of the terms used attending a poetry festival		

Communicating with Others

4.7   COMMUNICATING WITH ANOTHER PERSON

Interpersonal communication, or communicating with another person, is a two-way street. It involves both listening carefully and speaking clearly. Being an effective communicator when interacting with another person includes

- making eye contact and maintaining a relaxed posture
- providing feedback as you listen
- not interrupting
- rephrasing what the speaker says to show you understand
- controlling your emotions
- distinguishing between facts and opinions

EXERCISE

Rewriting a Dialogue

Read the following dialogue. Cross out four statements or actions that hinder effective communication. Then rewrite the statement or action so that it contributes to effective communication. Use the list of suggestions above to rewrite the dialogue.

Clint: Hey, Justin. We need to talk about finding a new location for the school recycling bins. You're the president of the recycling coalition. Have you got a minute?

Justin: (not looking up from his magazine) According to this article, scientists expect us to have a colony on Mars by the end of this century. Incredible!

_____

Clint: Ugh, great. In the meantime, the recycling bins need a place to stay. Got any ideas?

_____

Justin: I wonder what the colonists would do all day? I guess they'd be busy with experiments and stuff like that.

_____

Clint: Talking to you is like talking to a Martian. Earth to Justin, come in, Justin.

_____

Justin: What do you mean? I'm not a space cadet, I'm just interested in science, that's all.

_____

Clint: Well then, let's talk about the science of recycling. What are we—

_____

Justin: (holding up the magazine) —Wow, here's a drawing of what the Mars colony might look like!

_____

4.8 COMMUNICATING IN A SMALL GROUP

Communicating in a small group requires all the elements of effective communication between two people. But when you're working with a small group, it's also necessary to observe some other guidelines. These include:

- understanding helpful group roles, such as leader, secretary, gatekeeper, and harmonizer
- avoiding destructive roles, such as joker, dominator, blocker, and deserter
- respecting group norms, the rules that govern appropriate behavior for group members
- taking turns
- helping to create a positive group climate
- establishing group goals

EXERCISE

Evaluating a Small Group

Think of a small group you've participated in recently. Possibilities include a group project for a class, a committee, a sports team, a club, or any group outside of school. Use the scales on this page to analyze and rate your group on a number of different items. Place a check mark at the point on the scale that you feel corresponds to your group's grade on each item. Then give your group an overall letter grade for how well it communicates and write a short evaluation. Suggest ways this group could improve its communication. In the space labeled "Suggestions for improvement," identify both helpful and destructive roles taken by group members. What roles does the group need? Which should it try to eliminate?

Group members understand and respect group norms.

_____
A   B   C   D   F

Group members understand group roles.

_____
A   B   C   D   F

Group members take turns participating.

_____
A   B   C   D   F

Group members help to create a positive climate.

_____
A   B   C   D   F

Group members work together to establish group goals.

_____
A   B   C   D   F

Overall grade _____

Suggestions for improvement _____

_____

_____

_____

4.9 COMMUNICATING IN A LARGE GROUP

In the previous activity, you explored communication in a small group. Large groups require many of the same skills you use in a small group. But large groups also require special communication skills. Some of these skills are:

- sharing group roles so everyone can participate
- focusing on key relationships
- emphasizing group identify, norms, and goals to encourage cohesiveness
- standing up when speaking
- avoiding the pressure to conform, or "groupthink"
- taking and fostering responsibility

EXERCISE

Evaluating Large Group Communication

Read each of the following descriptions, Then, on the lines following the description, evaluate the group described. Is it succeeding at large-group communication? Which of the above skills is it using? Which is it lacking?

1. Although she rarely said anything in the meetings, one member of the committee stood and spoke with such authority that everyone listened to her and respected her opinion on the issue.

   _____

   _____

2. At first, the new proposal was very popular with almost all of the members. However, one member calmly objected and explained her reasoning. As a result, the group decided to reexamine the proposal, which was eventually rejected.

   _____

   _____

3. "I haven't even met most of the members of the project team," she explained, "but I have become good friends with the coordinator and several other members of our work group."

   _____

   _____

4. "I couldn't tell who was speaking," said one member of the assembly. "I was at the back of the room and I couldn't understand any of the words."

   _____

   _____

5. Even though many members disagreed with the committee's recommendation, they did not speak out at the meeting and the recommendation led to a plan of action they did not want.

   _____

   _____

6. "Our group is too large for one person to keep an eye on everything," one committee head explained. "But I just do my own job and take care of my own responsibilities. When other members see me doing this, I think it serves as a good example to them."

_____

_____

7. The group found that 17 of its members felt unappreciated because they weren't given anything to do. They watched as three people did most of the work.

_____

_____

8. Every member of the group was given a bumper sticker that said "Together we can make it happen."

_____

_____

9. One member of the school yearbook staff spent more time chatting with his friends than he did working with the other members of the staff to write the yearbook.

_____

_____

4.10 ASKING AND ANSWERING QUESTIONS

Knowing the most effective ways to ask and answer questions in a group can help you become a great communicator. Here are some guidelines to remember when *asking* questions.

- Wait to be recognized.
- Make your questions short, clear, and direct.
- Don't debate or argue with the speaker.
- Don't take too much of others' time.
- Don't give a speech yourself.

Here are some guidelines to remember when *answering* questions.

- Be prepared for a question-and-answer period.
- Be patient.
- Make your answers clear, short, and direct.
- Rephrase difficult questions.
- Be courteous.
- Try to handle difficult members of the audience gracefully.

EXERCISES

A. Asking Questions

Work with a partner. Review *The Very Brief Relation of the Devastation of the Indies* (pages 96–99 in your textbook) as if you were preparing give it as a speech to a group. Use the space below to write out answers to possible questions you might receive about your speech. Read the article to your partner. Then have him or her ask you several questions about your "speech." Answer your partner's questions, using the answers you prepared if possible.

_____

_____

_____

_____

_____

_____

_____

_____

_____

_____

_____

_____

_____

B. Answering Questions

Now switch roles with your partner. Have your partner review the first section of the excerpt from *The General History of Virginia* (up to "Leading an expedition on the Chickahominy River…") on pages 102–105 of your textbook and then give it as a speech, showing and explaining the noise level diagram. Your partner should prepare a list of possible questions and their answers. You should use the space below to jot down questions as your partner reads the "speech." Then, ask your questions and have your partner use the information prepared in advance to answer them. If your partner is unable to answer your questions, brainstorm sources you could consult to answer them.

_____

_____

_____

_____

_____

_____

_____

_____

_____

_____

_____

_____

_____

_____

_____

_____

_____

_____

Communication Styles and Cultural Barriers

4.11 BEING CONSIDERATE OF OTHER CULTURES AND COMMUNICATION STYLES

Learning about other individual people's communication styles can be a great help in becoming an effective communicator. Different cultures also emphasize different aspects of communication. The key rules when communicating with a person from another culture are to be aware that cultural communication differences do exist and to know and respect the person's cultural practices and behaviors.

EXERCISE

Learning about Cultural Communication Practices

The table on this page is designed to help you interview a person about his or her cultural communication style. First, choose a person to interview. Fill in the information at the top of the form. Then use the remaining space to jot down questions and the answers given by the person you interview. For example, your first question might be, "Tell me about a time you felt you experienced a miscommunication based on cultural differences." In other questions you might want to explore how the person became aware of cultural miscommunication and different communication styles, what these differences were, and how he or she tried to overcome them. Use extra sheets of paper if you need them. When you have completed your interview, use the information you collect to take part in a class discussion about how cultural backgrounds can influence communication.

Person Interviewed:	
Questions	**Answers**
1.	
2.	
3.	
4.	
5.	

4.12 OVERCOMING BARRIERS TO EFFECTIVE MULTICULTURAL COMMUNICATION

When people from different cultural backgrounds communicate, stumbling blocks can arise. Here are some guidelines you can follow to avoid these stumbling blocks.

- Treat every person as an individual; avoid stereotyping others.
- Be sensitive to sources of miscommunication.
- Seek common ground; focus on similarities between you and the other person, not your differences.
- Accept other people as they are, even if you have disagreements.
- Avoid provoking language.
- Use I-statements instead of you-statements.

EXERCISE

Evaluating Multicultural Communication

Read each of the following situations. On the lines below, write a short evaluation of each one, using the guidelines above. Point out the communication mistakes and suggest how the person could improve his or her multicultural communication.

1. Jeremy watched from the back of the room as the chairperson of the neighborhood committee called the meeting to order. The meeting had been called to try to deal with the problem of dogs running loose. Several older residents had complained to the police, and the community relations officer of the police department had suggested that the people in the neighborhood get together to discuss solutions to the problem. After several people had spoken, Jeremy stood up. "I think the solution to the problem is simple," he explained. "You older people have a hard time accepting dogs; they make noise and run around. My advice to you," he said to the senior citizens at the meeting, "is be a little more laid-back about it. If you didn't get so upset, then we wouldn't have a problem at all."

_____

_____

_____

_____

2. Ms. Alexander was sitting in her hotel room in Nairobi. It was her first business trip to Kenya, where her construction company did a lot of business. As an African American, she was especially proud and excited to be able to arrange deal that would bring jobs and business to an African country. She had just returned from a critical meeting with some important clients. As she thought back about the meeting, she felt confused. She had believed that the meeting was going very well up until the end. Then, suddenly, the clients became quite cool and reserved toward her, and she felt they were trying to hurry her away from the meeting. She suspected that she must have offended them in some way. "I have no idea what the problem is," she wondered to herself. "It must have been something I said or did, but I don't know what it is. How can I find out?"

_____

_____

_____

_____

3. Jennifer was completely at a loss about what to do. Ming, the daughter of one of her mother's business associates, was staying with them for several weeks. The girl, who was Jennifer's age, was from Taiwan, where her mother often went on business trips. The two girls could barely speak to each other. Jennifer sat on her bed, watching Ming. Ming was looking at the photographs of the basketball teams Jennifer had played on. As she looked at the team photos, Ming picked up Jennifer's basketball and started spinning it on her finger. Glumly, Jennifer thought to herself, "This is awful. I can't talk to her, she comes from a different country, I don't know what she's interested in, and I have no way of finding out. And on top of everything, I could be out playing basketball with my friends. Instead, I have to sit here and try to find out what this girl likes to do."

_____

_____

_____

_____

4.13 COLLABORATIVE LEARNING AND COMMUNICATION

Collaboration is the act of working with one or more other people to achieve a goal. Many common learning situations involve collaboration. Examples are discussions, small group projects, tutoring, and peer evaluations. When you are involved in collaborative learning situations, keep these suggestions in mind.

In discussion groups,

- listen actively.
- be polite.
- participate in the discussion.
- try to keep the discussion focused.
- in a formal discussion, assign roles.

When working on projects,

- choose a leader.
- set a goal.
- make a list of tasks and a schedule.
- make an assignment sheet.
- set times for future meetings.
- evaluate your overall success.

When tutoring,

- find out what the other student needs to learn.
- break your teaching down into steps.
- review basic information.
- give practice activities.
- be patient, encouraging, and supportive.

When being tutored,

- bring all the materials you will need.
- explain what you need help with.
- ask questions.
- be patient and polite.
- don't give up if you do not understand immediately.

Review the guidelines on self- and peer evaluation on pages 1047-48 of your textbook.

EXERCISE

Critiquing a Collaborative Learning Situation

The form on this page will help you critique a collaborative learning situation you have recently participated in. Fill in the information at the top of the form. Then complete the critique form.

Collaborative Learning Situation (circle one)

Small Group Discussion   Small Group Project   Tutoring   Peer Evaluation   Other

Number of participants: _____

Focus of situation: _____

_____

What went well in the situation? _____

_____

What went badly in the situation? _____

_____

How did I contribute? _____

_____

What could I have done better? _____

_____

Overall evaluation of the collaborative learning situation _____

_____

Communication Styles and Cultural Barriers

4.14 CONDUCTING AN INTERVIEW

When you're interviewing someone, planning is half the battle. By being prepared with background information on the subject and a list of questions, you can make sure that your interview will be a success. Other important elements of a successful interview include:

- setting up a time
- explaining who you are and why you want to interview the person
- asking open-ended questions, not ones that can be answered with a simple yes or no
- tape recording the interview in addition to taking notes
- writing down main points and recording key statements word for word
- ending the interview on time
- writing up your interview as soon as possible

EXERCISE

Planning and Conducting an Interview

In this activity, you'll interview a classmate on one of the following topics:

- an unforgettable experience
- someone the person especially admires and why
- the person's long term career plans or hopes

Use the form below to prepare and conduct your interview. Write prepared questions on the first set of lines in each group. The second set of lines is for you to take notes on the person's answers and copy key statements. Use extra paper if necessary.

Interview Subject _____ Interviewer _____ Date _____

Topic of Interview _____

Q _____

_____

A _____

_____

_____

_____

Q _____

_____

A _____

_____

Q _____

_____

A _____

_____

_____

_____

Q _____

_____

A _____

_____

_____

_____

Q _____

_____

A _____

_____

_____

_____

Public Speaking

4.15 GIVING A SPEECH

Giving a speech, whether a formal or an informal one, is a skill you will use many times in your life. Although some people are afraid of speaking in public, thorough preparation, practice, and positive thinking can overcome this fear. In this activity, you'll work with a small group of three or four people to practice your speechmaking skills.

EXERCISE

Brainstorming Ideas for a Speech

Have each member of your group choose a different quotation from the following list to use as the basis for a speech. Write the name of the person who has chosen the quotation in the boxes on the next page. Then, as a group, work together to brainstorm phrases, statements, and ideas that could be used in a speech based on the quotation. Takes notes in the boxes about each quotation.

1. "No man can put a chain about the ankle of his fellow man without at last finding the other end fastened about his own neck." (Frederick Douglass)

2. "There are two ways of spreading light: to be the candle or the mirror that reflects it." (Edith Wharton)

3. "They paved paradise and put up a parking lot." (Joni Mitchell)

4. "Be not angry that you cannot make others as you wish them to be, since you cannot make yourself as you wish to be." (Thomas à Kempis)

5. "Little strokes fell great oaks." (Benjamin Franklin)

6. "You have not converted a man because you have silenced him." (Viscount Morley)

7. "National injustice is the surest road to national downfall." (William Gladstone)

8. "One man with courage makes a majority." (Andrew Jackson)

Quotation #1	Quotation #2
Quotation #3	Quotation #4
Quotation #5	Quotation #6
Quotation #7	Quotation #8

4.16 TYPES OF SPEECHES

There are three main types of speeches:

- An **impromptu** speech is given without any preparation.
- A **memorized** speech is one that has been written and memorized.
- An **extemporaneous** speech is one in which the speaker refers to notes occasionally.

EXERCISE

Giving an Impromptu Speech

For this activity, look back at the list of eight quotations in activity 4.15. Your group brainstormed ideas for three or four of the quotations. Choose one of the quotations your group did not brainstorm ideas for. Then present to the group a short impromptu speech based on the quotation you choose. Make extra copies of the form below and use them to evaluate the impromptu speeches of the other members of your group. Share your evaluations with the other members.

Speaker _____

Subject _____

Delivery

Nonverbal delivery (eye contact, facial expressions, gestures, posture, proximity)

_____

_____

Verbal delivery (volume, pitch, pace, tone, enunciation) _____

_____

_____

Mode of delivery (comfort/confidence, extemporaneous delivery) _____

_____

_____

Design

Introduction (gains attention, introduces audience to topic, states main idea clearly, previews clearly)

_____

_____

Conclusion (provides appropriate conclusion, summarizes, is memorable)

_____

_____

Organization (clear and simple, appropriate organizational pattern, easy to follow)

_____

_____

Content

Achieves purpose (to inform, persuade, entertain, etc.)

_____

_____

Supporting materials (details support main point, uses good examples)

_____

_____

Other Comments _____

_____

_____

_____

4.17 STEPS IN PREPARING AN EXTEMPORANEOUS SPEECH

In an extemporaneous speech, the speaker refers occasionally to notes. The outline form on this page will help you plan and prepare to give an extemporaneous speech based on the quotation you chose in activity 4.15. Each section of the form corresponds to a step in the process of preparing an extemporaneous speech, which you will give to your group in the next activity.

EXERCISE

Preparing an Extemporaneous Speech

Complete the form. In the first section, for example, you should write in your own words the topic of the speech you are planning based on the quotation you chose in activity 4.15.

1. Choose a topic

   _____

   A. Consider the audience _____

   B. What are my strengths as a speaker? _____

   _____

   C. What are my weaknesses as a speaker? _____

   _____

2. Prewrite to identify what I know and think about the topic and how I can approach it.

   _____

   _____

   _____

   _____

   _____

   _____

3. Research the topic. What are some sources and references I could look at? _____

   _____

   _____

4. Determine the purpose of the speech: demonstrate, inform, compare, persuade?

   _____

   _____

5. Organize the material

   A. What are the main points of the speech?

   _____

   _____

   _____

   _____

   B. What organizational strategy seems most appropriate?

   _____

   _____

   _____

   _____

6. Which visual aids would be useful for my topic? _____

   _____

   _____

7. Prepare note cards

8. Rehearse the speech with mirror or tape recorder

4.18 GUIDELINES FOR GIVING A SPEECH

A speech should always include an **introduction** (beginning), **body** (middle), and **conclusion** (end). The introduction of your speech should spark the audience's interest, present your central idea, and briefly preview your main points. The body of your speech should expand on each of your main points in order to support the central idea. The conclusion of your speech should be memorable and give your audience a sense of completion. Below are tips for successful public speaking.

- **Be sincere and enthusiastic.** Your enthusiasm—or lack of enthusiasm—will spread to your audience.
- **Maintain good but relaxed posture.** Don't slouch or lean. Move around a bit to release normal nervous tension. Keep your hands free to gesture naturally instead of gripping notecards, props, or the podium.
- **Speak slowly.** Spoken words are more difficult than written language and visual images for audiences to process. Practice pausing. Don't be afraid of silence. Focus on communicating with the audience. By looking for feedback, you will pace yourself appropriately.
- **Maintain genuine eye contact.** Treat the audience as individuals, not as a mass of people. Look at individual faces.
- **Speak in a genuine, relaxed, conversational tone.** Don't act or stiffen up. Just be yourself.
- **Communicate.** Focus on conveying your message, not "getting through" the speech.
- **Use strategic pauses.** Pausing allows important information to sink in.
- **Remain confident and composed.** Remember that listeners generally want you to succeed. To overcome initial nervousness, take two or three deep breaths as you are stepping up to speak.

EXERCISE

Giving a Speech

As each member of your group gives his or her speech, evaluate it using the chart on the following page. After each speech, share your feedback with the speaker. Remember to include suggestions that will help the speaker improve his or her communication skills.

Categories	Speaker: Subject:	Speaker: Subject:	Speaker: Subject:
Verbal delivery (volume, pitch, pace, tone, enunciation)			
Nonverbal delivery (eye contact, facial expressions, gestures, posture, proximity)			
Mode of delivery (comfort/confidence, extemporaneous delivery)			
Introduction (gains attention, introduces audience to topic, states main idea clearly, previews clearly)			
Conclusion (provides appropriate conclusion, summarizes, is memorable)			
Organization (clear and simple, appropriate organizational pattern, easy to follow)			
Achieves purpose (to inform, persuade, entertain, etc.)			
Supporting materials (details support main point, uses good examples)			
Other Comments			
Overall Evaluation			

4.19 ORAL INTERPRETATION

Oral interpretation is the art of presenting a literary work aloud to an audience. One type of oral interpretation is the dramatic interpretation of poetry. To prepare a dramatic interpretation of poetry, follow these basic steps:

- Read the poem as many times as necessary to gain a thorough understanding of it.
- Determine the type of poem you are reading—lyric, narrative, or dramatic. Review the characteristics of each kind of poem on page 1097 of your textbook.
- Analyze the speaker and characters of the poem.
- Practice elements of verbal and nonverbal communication.
- Mark up a copy of the poem, noting where you will change your pace, volume, or voice. Also note what emotions you want to express at specific points.
- Memorize the poem.
- Rehearse your interpretation, adding appropriate facial expressions and gestures.

EXERCISES

A. Preparing a Poem for Oral Interpretation

Choose a poem from your textbook, or a favorite from another source. Use the following questionnaire to prepare it for oral interpretation. Complete each line that is applicable to your poem.

Poem _____

Author _____

Type (circle one)   Lyric   Narrative   Dramatic

Analysis of speaker or narrator

Age, gender, other characteristics _____

_____

Speaker's or narrator's situation _____

_____

Speaker's or narrator's emotions, values, beliefs, or hopes _____

_____

Does the reader know more about the speaker's or narrator's situation than the narrator does? Explain.

_____

_____

Other notes on the speaker or narrator _____

_____

Analysis of other characters in the poem

List _____

_____

_____

_____

_____

_____

Using verbal and nonverbal communication to interpret the poem

Gestures, facial expressions, and voice qualities to represent the speaker or narrator

_____

_____

_____

_____

_____

Gestures, facial expressions, and voice qualities to represent the other characters

_____

_____

_____

_____

_____

_____

_____

_____

_____

_____

B. Orally Interpreting a Poem

Use the answers to the questionnaire to mark up a copy of your poem. Then read your poem to the class, including all the elements of oral interpretation you have decided to add. You may also want to tape-record or videotape the performances to compile a class archive.

4.20 TELLING A STORY

Telling stories is an ancient art, one that many people still enjoy today. When telling a story, keep these elements in mind:

- Decide on your purpose.
- Select a focus.
- Choose your point of view.
- Determine the sequence and duration of events.
- Carefully select the details to describe.
- Choose vivid, concrete characters.
- Create interesting dialogue.

EXERCISES

A. Preparing a Story for Telling

Choose one of the short stories in your textbook, or a favorite from another source. Review the discussion of how to tell a story on pages 1098-99 of your textbook. Read the story enough times so that you know it well enough to retell in your own words. Then use the following form to analyze and prepare to retell the story.

Story: _____

Author: _____

Purpose in telling the story _____

_____

_____

Focus _____

_____

_____

Point of view _____

_____

_____

Sequence of events _____

_____

_____

Duration of events _____

_____

_____

Details to emphasize _____

_____

_____

Characters to include (justify deletions, changes, etc.) _____

_____

_____

_____

_____

_____

Dialogue

Gestures, facial expressions, and voice qualities to represent the characters _____

_____

_____

_____

Explain and justify decisions to change, simplify, eliminate, or expand some of the dialogue _____

_____

_____

_____

_____

_____

Other considerations: _____

_____

_____

_____

_____

B. Telling a Story

Use the information you supplied above to prepare to tell your story. Then tell your story to the class, including all the elements of oral interpretation and story-telling skills you have decided to add. You may also want to tape-record or videotape the performances to compile a class archive.

4.21 PARTICIPATING IN A DEBATE

A debate is a contest with special rules in which two people or groups of people defend opposite sides of a proposition in an attempt to convince a judge or audience to agree with their views. As you prepare for and participate in a debate, follow these suggestions:

- Be prepared. Research your argument. Also be aware of your opponent's side of the issue so you can better argue against his or her statements.
- Be organized. Try to follow a logical organizational pattern to avoid confusing the audience, judge, or other team.
- Take notes. During the debate, record your opponent's arguments so you can better argue against them.
- Be audience-centered. Don't get so involved in the argument with your opponent that you forget that your main duty is to convince the audience or judge that your argument is correct.

EXERCISE

Preparing for a Debate

With a partner, select one of the following debate issues. Each of you should take an opposite side of the issue you choose.

- Large-scale immigration provides many benefits to the United States and should be continued.
- Affirmative action is wrong and merely continues the injustices of the past.
- The teaching of music, art, dance, and other non-academic subjects in schools is a waste of valuable school time.
- Stricter gun control will not reduce violent crime.
- Medical testing on animals makes a valuable contribution to science and should be expanded.

Use the form on this page to prepare your arguments. When you have finished, work with your partner to evaluate each other's preparation.

Proposition: Resolved: _____

Type (circle one):   Fact   Value   Policy

My position (circle one):   Affirmative (in favor of)   Negative (against)

My main arguments in order of importance:

1. _____

_____

2. _____

_____

3. _____

_____

4. _____

_____

5. _____

_____

Reference sources to consult to support my argument:

_____

_____

_____

_____

_____

_____

Opponent's probable main arguments and my counter-arguments:

_____

_____

_____

_____

_____

_____

_____

Possible cross-examination questions:

_____

_____

_____

_____

_____

_____

4.22 PREPARING A MULTIMEDIA PRESENTATION

In the worlds of business, education, industry, and government, multimedia presentations have become the standard way of communicating information. The use of charts, transparencies, video, audio, and computer software programs like PowerPoint do a great job of communicating a lot of information quickly and effectively. Knowing how to use these powerful tools will make you a better communicator. When you are planning a multimedia presentation, remember to:

- make sure that your audio-visual elements really make your presentation better and will increase the audience's understanding.
- make sure your presentation is clearly audible and visible from everywhere in the room—not too soft, blurry, dark, or small.
- get to know the equipment you'll be using. Have a backup plan in case of equipment malfunction.
- check beforehand to see that the room you'll be in can accommodate your needs and that you will have all the accessories you need in place.

EXERCISE

Planning a Multimedia Presentation

Begin by choosing a topic for a multimedia presentation on any suitable subject. You might consider a figure or event from history or current events, an artist, musician, athlete, or scientist, a business or industry, a hobby, or anything that can be presented in an audio-visual presentation. Then use the form on this page to plan your presentation.

Subject: _____

_____

Focus of presentation: _____

_____

Brief outline of presentation: _____

_____

_____

_____

_____

_____

_____

_____

_____

_____

_____

_____

Multimedia elements to use and equipment needed: _____

_____

_____

_____

_____

_____

_____

_____

_____

_____

_____

_____

Things to check in facility: _____

_____

_____

_____

_____

Other notes: _____

_____

_____

_____

_____

_____

_____

_____

_____

_____

Answer Key

4.1   VERBAL AND NONVERBAL COMMUNICATION

A. Students should show an understanding of why changes are made in volume, melody or pitch, pace, and tone at different places in the poem, as well as of the importance of clear enunciation. Evaluations should be accurate and fair.

B. *Responses may vary. Possible responses are given.*

Anger: lean threateningly toward audience, stand up very straight, make angry, threatening gestures, frown, glare at audience

Curiosity: move closer to audience, raise eyebrows, open eyes wide, tilt head, purse lips, lean over, reach toward audience

Fear: make eyes wide, express horror with hands and arms, stiffen posture, lean away from audience, push away with arms, mouth scream

Nervousness: glance quickly from side to side, look at watch, tap foot, fidget with fingers, make quick motions

4.2   ACTIVE VERSUS PASSIVE LISTENING

A. In the first exchange, Mikayla has not thought about what Andrey has said, in the second she dominates the conversation and becomes emotional, in the third she jumps to a conclusion about what Andrey says, and in the fourth, she becomes excited and talks to another person. In all four Mikayla might have provided feedback or rephrased Andrey's words, thought about his questions, used body language and eye contact to show she is listening, and controlled her own emotions.

B. *Responses will vary. Possible responses are given.*

1. Computers can be so frustrating! Getting a document to print depends on a lot of different things that all have to work right.
2. Here's how: click on Status on the Print icon. Then you'll see if there are any documents in the queue.
3. Sure, you could do that, but let's try one more thing before we reboot, OK?
4. I know. Let's ask Ms. Chang. She'll know what to do. She always has the answer to a computer problem.

4.3   LISTENING TO A LECTURE OR DEMONSTRATION

Responses will vary. Responses are given for the first one-and-a-half pages of "Why I Am Optimistic about America" (textbook pages 1006–1010).

1. A person could use this information to begin thinking about his or her own feelings about the future of the United States.
2. At the line, "the United States is a very special place, unique in special ways."
3. The United States is a very special place (its history is unique); there are good reasons to be optimistic about the future (Boorstin's early experiences in Tulsa and his understanding of American history).
4. Why do free societies tend to exaggerate their vices? Is it correct that the United States "need not be governed by the same expectations or plagued by the same problems that had afflicted people elsewhere"? Is American exceptionalism false?

4.4   LISTENING IN CONVERSATIONS

Students' dialogues should show and reflect an understanding of an assortment of the recommended techniques and mistakes to avoid described in the textbook on page 1088 and the activity.

4.5   LISTENING TO THE MEDIA

Students' evaluations should accurately identify and examine the program's use of facts and opinions, its quality with regard to acting, writing, directing and production elements (as applicable), and its messages and how they are communicated; overall evaluations should reflect students' standards and values.

4.6   ADAPTING LISTENING SKILLS TO SPECIFIC TASKS

Responses will vary. Possible responses are given.
1. Listening critically / watching a TV commercial, listening to a radio news editorial, listening to a candidates' debate
2. Listening for comprehension / getting instructions on how to find a friend's house, receiving directions on how to download music from the Internet, a sales talk about leasing versus buying cars
3. Listening to learn vocabulary / going on a nature walk to identify and name birds, presentation on flying radio-controlled planes and the names of important parts in a plane, a presentation on different words and terms used in motocross bicycle racing
4. Listening for appreciation / attending a storytellers' convention, gathering to sing folk songs, watching a play

4.7   COMMUNICATING WITH ANOTHER PERSON

Students should correct four statements or actions in the original. *Possible responses are given.*

Clint: *(looking up from his magazine)* Sure, I've got some ideas about where we might put the recycling bins.

Clint: *(sitting down) Here's my idea. How about putting them near the dish line in the cafeteria?*

Justin: *(nodding his head) That's a good idea. It seems like the obvious place for recycling lunch stuff. What about also putting a bin near the gym?*

Clint: *I like it. Kids who eat stuff at basketball games would have a place to separate trash from recyclable things.*

Justin: *How about football and soccer games? Think we could get another bin and put it out near the concession stand?*

Clint: *I don't see why not. We're going to have to come up with a plan to get rid of all this stuff we'll be collecting.*

Justin: *I've been thinking about that. I'll check on a few things and let you know what I find out.*

4.8   COMMUNICATING IN A SMALL GROUP

Students' evaluations should accurately reflect the small group's performance and communication abilities. Suggestions for improvements and grading should show understanding of the elements of small group communication discussed on pages 1090-91 of the textbook, including the helpful and destructive roles.

4.9   COMMUNICATING IN A LARGE GROUP

1. By standing and speaking firmly, the speaker is able to make her point.
2. This group was able to avoid "groupthink," or the pressure to conform, because one member voiced a different opinion.
3. This group is succeeding at having members focus on key relationships.
4. Group members should stand when they speak so others can see and hear them; a microphone would also help.
5. The group was not able to avoid "groupthink," or the pressure to conform; members should have spoken out about their disagreement.
6. Group members are fostering responsibility by doing their own jobs and encouraging others to do theirs.
7. This group should try to do a better job of sharing group roles.
8. The group succeeded in emphasizing group identity and goals.
9. The group member failed to focus on the key relationships he needed to focus on and neglected his responsibilities.

4.10 ASKING AND ANSWERING QUESTIONS

A. *Responses will vary. Possible responses are given.*

Why did most of the Spaniards in the new world treat the native peoples so terribly? (Their greed for gold and other riches made them exploit the native peoples.) Why did Bartolemé de las Casas have a different attitude about the native peoples that other Spaniards enslaved and tortured? (His religious convictions led him to believe they deserved better treatment.) How much success did Bartolemé de las Casas have in convincing other Spaniards to treat the native peoples better? Why? (Very little, since many Spaniards did not consider them to be their equals.)

B. *Responses will vary. Possible responses are given.*

What diseases did the colonists suffer from? Why did the native peoples give food to the English colonists? What reasons does John Smith give for the colonists' desperate situation? What happened to the deposed president? Sources of information are encyclopedias, history textbooks, books about the early history of Virginia and colonial America, history magazines, and the Internet.

4.11 BEING CONSIDERATE OF OTHER CULTURES AND COMMUNICATION STYLES

Students' question-and-answer forms should contain appropriate questions and conscientiously recorded answers. Students should use their information to take part in the class discussion.

4.12 OVERCOMING BARRIERS TO EFFECTIVE MULTICULTURAL COMMUNICATION

1. Jeremy makes several communication mistakes: he stereotypes older people as not being "laid-back" enough, uses provocative language and you-statements, and seems to blame them for the "problem," when, in fact, the problem is caused by the dogs and their owners who allow them to run loose.

2. Ms. Alexander probably said or did something that is considered impolite by her Kenyan clients. She might have prepared better for the meeting by learning about Kenyan customs. Also, in order to learn about the sources of this miscommunication, she could ask her Kenyan clients what she said or did to offend them. Then she could be more sensitive in the future and try not to make the same verbal or nonverbal communication mistake.

3. Jennifer is focusing on the differences between her and Ming, rather than considering the one striking similarity they share: both are interested in basketball. Jennifer should invite Ming to go play basketball with her friends as a way of breaking down the barriers between them.

4.13 COLLABORATIVE LEARNING AND COMMUNICATION

Students' completed critique charts should be thoughtful, accurate, and appropriate and should show an understanding of the elements of collaborative learning discussed on pages 1093-94 of the text.

4.14 CONDUCTING AN INTERVIEW

Students' interviews should reflect careful planning, conscientious note-taking, care with recording quotations, and understanding of the elements of conducting an interview discussed on pages 1094-95 of the textbook.

4.15 GIVING A SPEECH

Responses will vary. Possible responses for quotation #1 are given.

If one person is not free, then no one is free; slaves and slaveholders are tied together, all people are united whether they know it or not

4.16 TYPES OF SPEECHES

Students' speeches should reflect understanding of the elements of an impromptu speech, as discussed on p. 1095 of the textbook, as well as of the elements of verbal and nonverbal communication described on page 1 in the Speaking and Listening Resource. Evaluations should show careful consideration of the speeches and reflect understanding of the elements of impromptu speechmaking.

4.17 STEPS IN PREPARING AN EXTEMPORANEOUS SPEECH

Students' outlines should restate the topic based on the quotation, include information appropriate to their topic, accurately assess strengths and weaknesses, include suggestions for research, and choose an appropriate organizational strategy and visual aids.

4.18 GUIDELINES FOR GIVING A SPEECH

Students' evaluations and the follow-up discussion should reflect careful attention to the speeches, knowledge of the elements of good extemporaneous speech practices, and a positive, supportive tone.

4.19 ORAL INTERPRETATION OF POETRY

Students' questionnaires and readings should show understanding of the elements of oral interpretation as discussed on pages 1097-98 of the textbook and in the activity introduction and should be suitably adapted to the chosen poem.

4.20 TELLING A STORY

Students' questionnaires and story presentations should show understanding of the elements of oral interpretation as discussed on pages 1097-98 of the textbook and of story-telling on pages 1098-99. These elements should be appropriately adapted to the chosen story.

4.21 PARTICIPATING IN A DEBATE

Responses will vary. Possible responses are given. Students' preparation should be thoughtful, comprehensive, and appropriate.

"Large-scale immigration provides many benefits to the United States and should be continued." (policy)—Affirmative:

Main arguments: Because of its immigration policies, the United States is able to attract the most gifted and talented of the world's people, who want to live in this country and reap its benefits; since these people are often educated in their own countries, the United States gains the benefit of their skills without the expense of having to train them; immigrants such as Albert Einstein, Alfred Hitchcock, and Henry Kissinger have made tremendous contributions to our nation's well-being, defense, artistic and cultural life, and standard of living; ordinary immigrants bring with them new ways of living, thinking, and eating, all of which enrich our nation immeasurably.

Reference sources: state and Federal statistics, Internet websites, books and articles by supporters of immigration and multiculturalism, interviews with successful immigrants, public opinion polls

Opponent's arguments and answers: The United States is becoming too crowded and should restrict immigration (the United States' population density is low compared to most other developed countries); Immigrants take more from our national resources than they give (this is an opinion; cite facts that show contributions of immigrants); Immigrants commit crimes, take jobs from native-born Americans, and go on welfare (statistics do not support this view); Immigrants are not "true" Americans and dilute the national culture (all Americans except Native Americans are immigrants, American culture is made up of all the different cultures of its immigrant groups).

Possible cross-examination questions: Are you prepared to spend the extra huge amounts of money necessary to educate native-born Americans if you restrict the entry of highly educated immigrants? How will you decide which few immigrants to let into the country? What kind of country would we be living in today if we had not had the contributions of immigrants?

4.22 PREPARING A MULTIMEDIA PRESENTATION

Responses will vary. Students should complete the planning form with appropriate answers that show an understanding of the elements of a multimedia presentation as discussed on page 1100 of the textbook. A sample response for a presentation on Chief Joseph, the Nez Percé leader:

Focus: What has made Chief Joseph (In-mut-too-yah-lat-lat) so well known and respected?

Outline: Joseph's life and early history, the way of life of the Nez Percé, their growing conflicts with Europeans, the flight to Canada and Joseph's famous speech; his legacy

Multimedia elements needed: Overhead projector and transparencies, cassette player and sound system for background music, video equipment to show highlights from film documentary about Chief Joseph, large map with route and homelands marked, photos, props like Native American artifacts

Things to check: good location for speakers, video/TV unit, and screen for transparencies, enough outlets for all electrical equipment, need podium for me to speak behind

Other notes: Need to find or record the "I Will Fight No More Forever" speech to play for audience; ask Philip to demonstrate tribal dances